HAL•LEONARD

JAZZ PLAY ALONG

Book and CD for B♭, E♭ and C Instruments

Arranged and Produced by Mark Taylor

Essen
Jazz Cla

10 ESSENTIAL JAZZ CLASSICS

HAL LEONARD EUROPE
DISTRIBUTED BY MUSIC SALES

BOOK

CD

Exclusive Distributors:
Music Sales Limited
8/9 Frith Street, London W1D 3JB, England.

Order No. HLE90002462
ISBN 1-84609-115-2

Printed in the USA

Your Guarantee of Quality
As publishers, we strive to produce every book to the highest commercial standards.
This book has been carefully designed to minimise awkward page turns and to make playing from it a real pleasure.
Throughout, the printing and binding have been planned to ensure a sturdy, attractive publication which should give years of enjoyment.
If your copy fails to meet our high standards, please inform us and we will gladly replace it.

www.musicsales.com

Essential Jazz Classics

Volume 12

Arranged and Produced by
Mark Taylor

Featured Players:

Graham Breedlove–Trumpet
John Desalme–Alto Sax & Tenor Sax
Tony Nalker–Piano
Jim Roberts–Bass
Steve Fidyk–Drums

Recorded at Bias Studios, Springfield, Virginia
Bob Dawson, Engineer

HOW TO USE THE CD:

Each song has <u>two</u> tracks:

1) Split Track/Melody

Woodwind, Brass, Keyboard, and **Mallet Players** can use this track as a learning tool for melody style and inflection.

Bass Players can learn and perform with this track – remove the recorded bass track by turning down the volume on the LEFT channel.

Keyboard and **Guitar Players** can learn and perform with this track – remove the recorded piano part by turning down the volume on the RIGHT channel.

2) Full Stereo Track

Soloists or **Groups** can learn and perform with this accompaniment track with the RHYTHM SECTION only.

AIREGIN

BY SONNY ROLLINS

THE FRIM FRAM SAUCE

CD
3: SPLIT TRACK/MELODY
4: FULL STEREO TRACK
C VERSION

WORDS AND MUSIC BY
JOE RICARDEL AND REDD EVANS

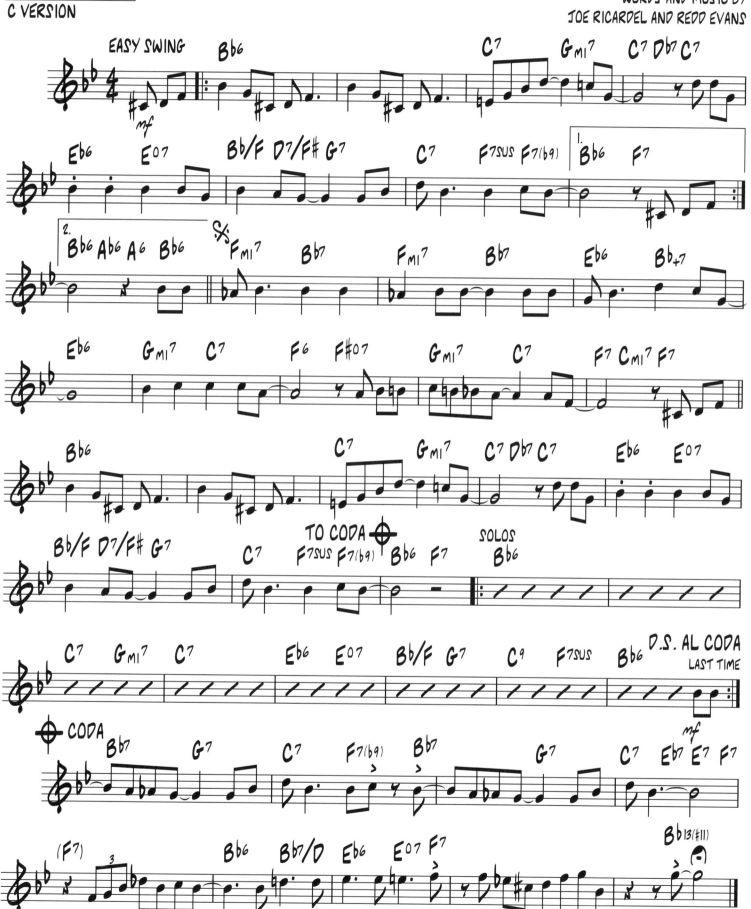

THE JIVE SAMBA

CD

5 : SPLIT TRACK/MELODY
6 : FULL STEREO TRACK

BY NAT ADDERLEY

C VERSION

MILESTONES

CD

◆ 7 : SPLIT TRACK/MELODY
◆ 8 : FULL STEREO TRACK

C VERSION

BY MILES DAVIS

NEFERTITI

BY WAYNE SHORTER

C VERSION

RED CLAY

BY FREDDIE HUBBARD

CD
🔶13 : SPLIT TRACK/MELODY
🔶14 : FULL STEREO TRACK

C VERSION

PHASE DANCE

CD

15 : SPLIT TRACK/MELODY
16 : FULL STEREO TRACK

SONG FOR MY FATHER

C VERSION

BY HORACE SILVER

THINK ON ME

BY GEORGE CABLES

WINDOWS

CD
◆ 19 : SPLIT TRACK/MELODY
◆ 20 : FULL STEREO TRACK

BY CHICK COREA

C VERSION

MED JAZZ WALTZ

TO CODA ⊕

SOLOS (2 CHORUSES)

AIREGIN

Bb VERSION

BY SONNY ROLLINS

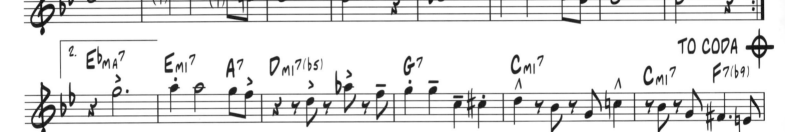

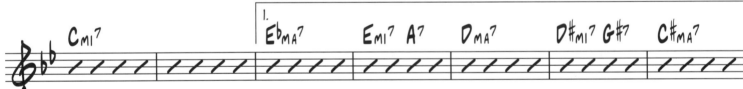

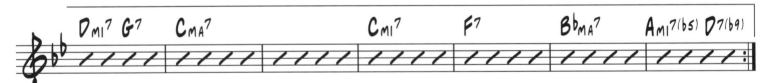

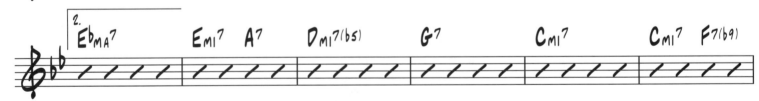

THE FRIM FRAM SAUCE

WORDS AND MUSIC BY
JOE RICARDEL AND REDD EVANS

Bb VERSION

THE JIVE SAMBA

BY NAT ADDERLEY

Bb VERSION

MILESTONES

CD
- **7** : SPLIT TRACK/MELODY
- **8** : FULL STEREO TRACK

Bb VERSION

BY MILES DAVIS

NEFERTITI

CD
◆9 : SPLIT TRACK/MELODY
◆10 : FULL STEREO TRACK

Bb VERSION

BY WAYNE SHORTER

MEDIUM SWING

SOLOS

D.C. AL FINE
NO REPEAT

RED CLAY

PHASE DANCE

BY PAT METHENY
AND LYLE MAYS

Bb VERSION

LATIN-EVEN 8THS

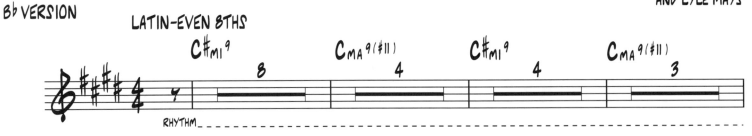

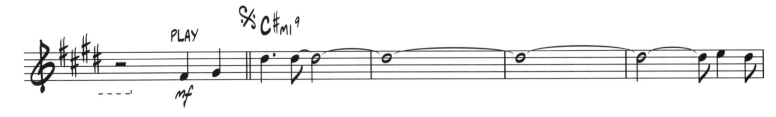

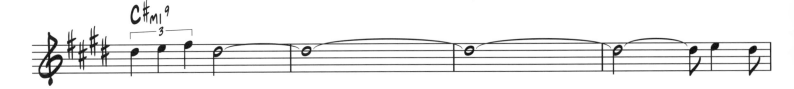

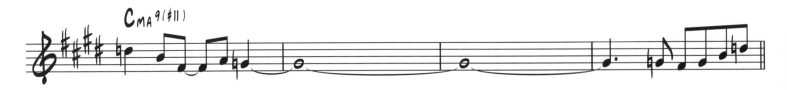

TO CODA ⊕

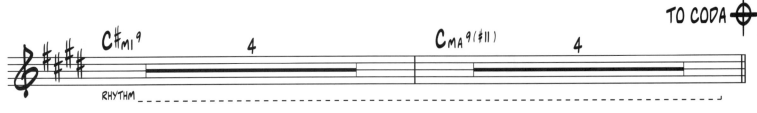

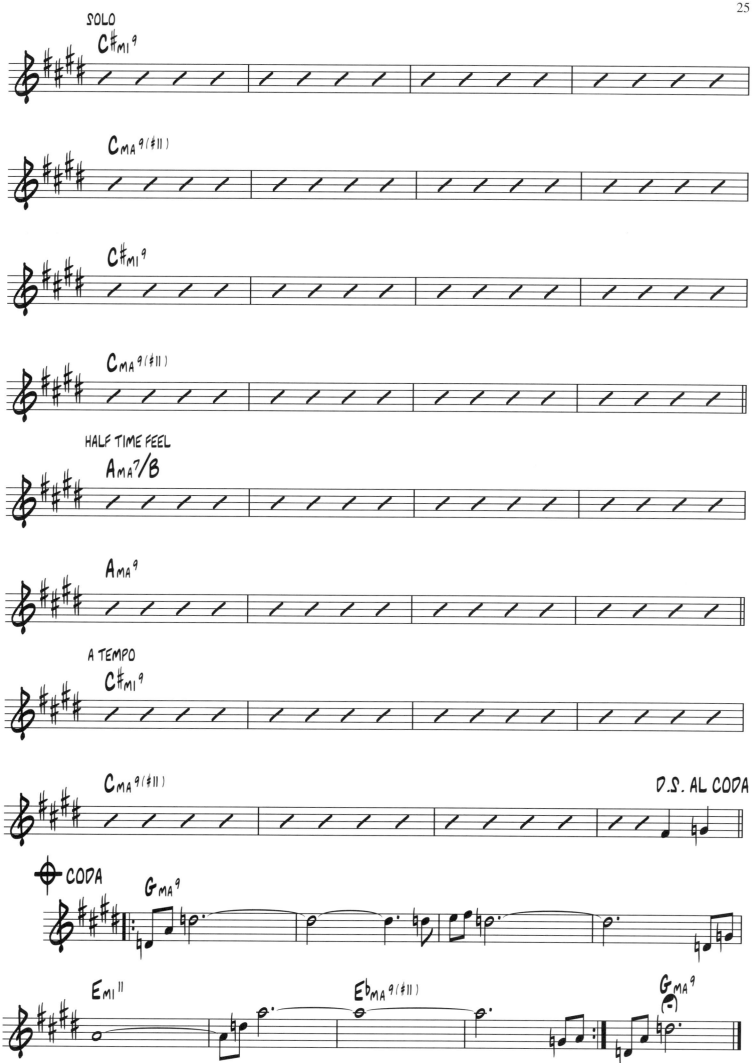

CD

SONG FOR MY FATHER

BY HORACE SILVER

Bb VERSION

THINK ON ME

CD
17 : SPLIT TRACK/MELODY
18 : FULL STEREO TRACK

BY GEORGE CABLES

Bb VERSION

MED JAZZ ROCK

WINDOWS

BY CHICK COREA

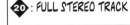

AIREGIN

BY SONNY ROLLINS

Eb VERSION

THE FRIM FRAM SAUCE

WORDS AND MUSIC BY
JOE RICARDEL AND REDD EVANS

Eb VERSION

THE JIVE SAMBA

By Nat Adderley

MILESTONES

E♭ Version

BY MILES DAVIS

NEFERTITI

Eb VERSION

BY WAYNE SHORTER

RED CLAY

PHASE DANCE

CD

11 : SPLIT TRACK/MELODY
12 : FULL STEREO TRACK

E♭ VERSION

BY PAT METHENY
AND LYLE MAYS

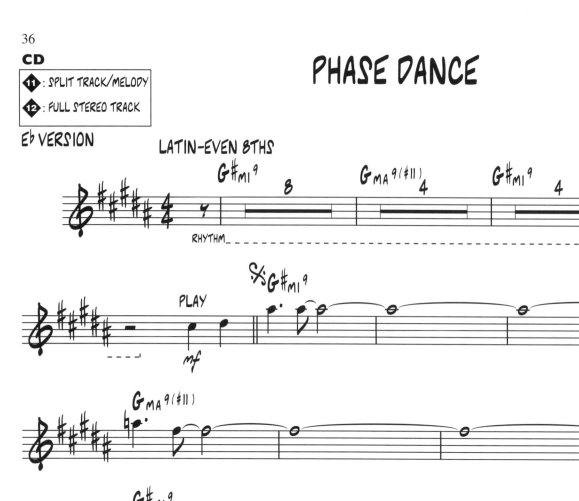

TO CODA ⊕

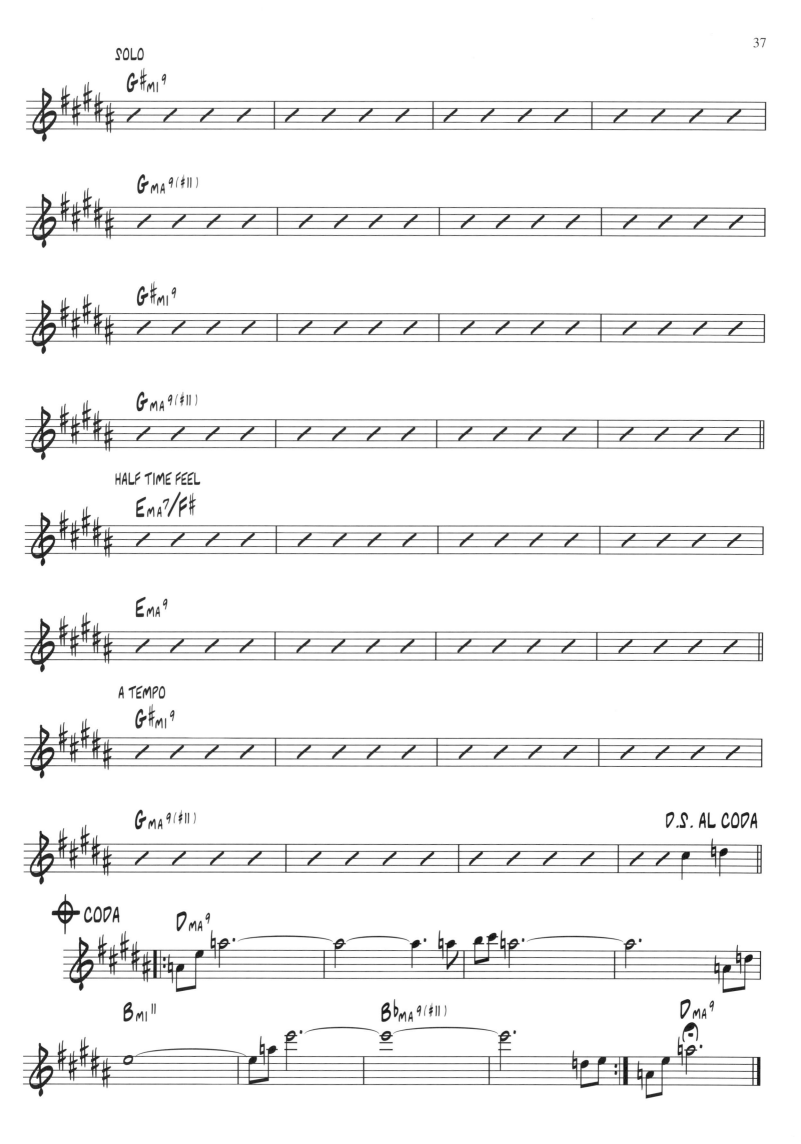

SONG FOR MY FATHER

CD
15 : SPLIT TRACK/MELODY
16 : FULL STEREO TRACK

Eb VERSION

BY HORACE SILVER

THINK ON ME

BY GEORGE CABLES

Eb VERSION

WINDOWS

BY CHICK COREA

CD
- ◆19 : SPLIT TRACK/MELODY
- ◆20 : FULL STEREO TRACK

E♭ VERSION

AIREGIN

BY SONNY ROLLINS

THE FRIM FRAM SAUCE

WORDS AND MUSIC BY
JOE RICARDEL AND REDD EVANS

THE JIVE SAMBA

BY NAT ADDERLEY

🎼 C VERSION

LATIN

SOLOS (2 FULL CHORUSES)

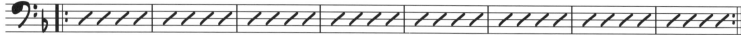

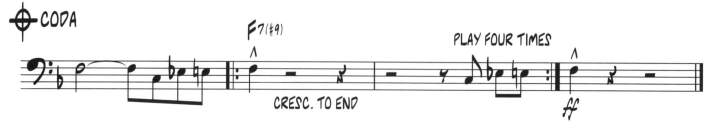

MILESTONES

BY MILES DAVIS

NEFERTITI

BY WAYNE SHORTER

𝄢: C VERSION

RED CLAY

CD

PHASE DANCE

BY PAT METHENY
AND LYLE MAYS

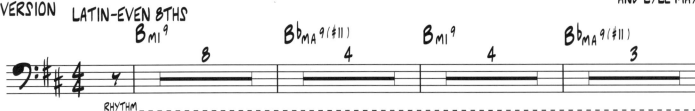

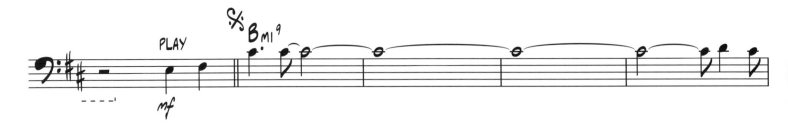

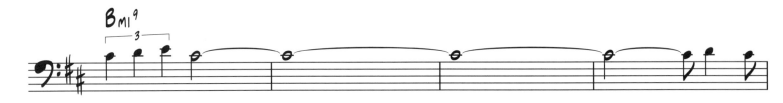

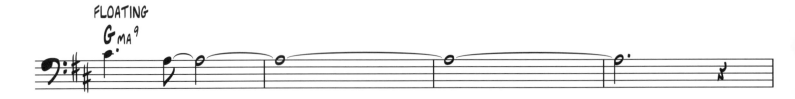

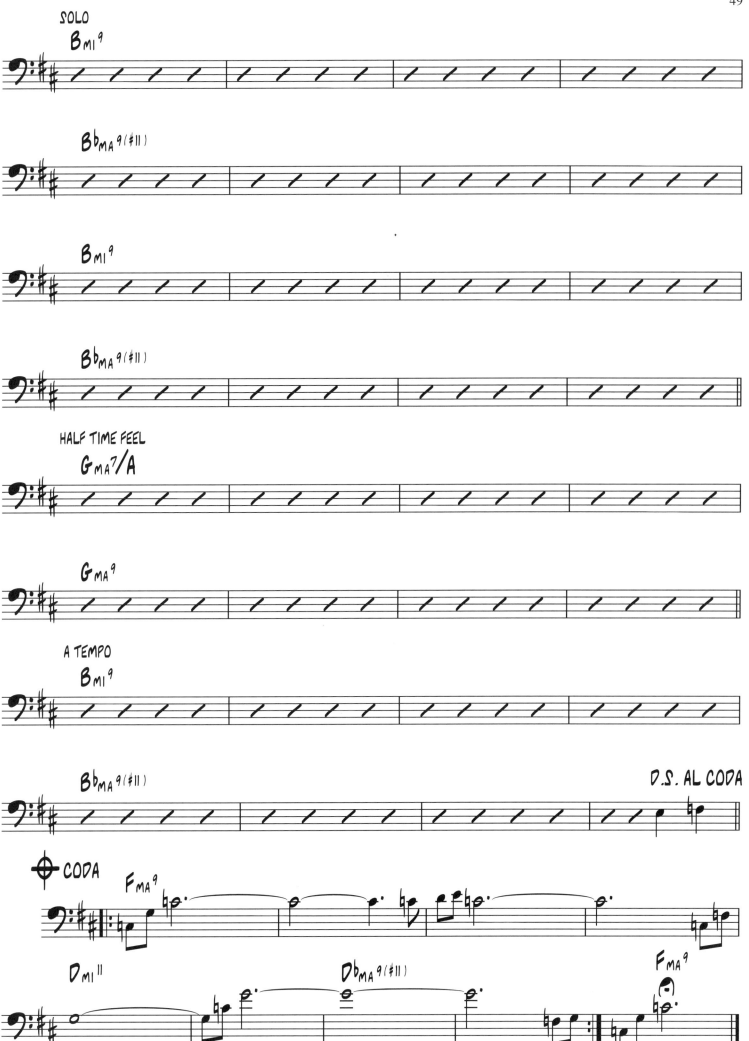

Song for My Father

BY HORACE SILVER

THINK ON ME

BY GEORGE CABLES

CD
17 : SPLIT TRACK/MELODY
18 : FULL STEREO TRACK

𝄢: C VERSION

CD

WINDOWS

BY CHICK COREA

𝄢: C VERSION

MED JAZZ WALTZ

SOLOS (2 CHORUSES)

Bmi7 · · · · | · · · · | · · · · | · · · · | G#mi7(b5) · · · · | · · · · |

C#7 · · · · | F#mi7 · · · · | · · · · | · · · · | · · · · | · · · · |

D7sus · · · · | · · · · | · · · · | · · · · | Ema7 · · · · | · · · · |

Ema7(#11) · · · · | · · · · | · · · · | · · · · | · · · · | · · · · |

Ab7 · · · · | A7 · · · · | Ab7 · · · · | A7 · · · · | Ab7 · · · · | A7 · · · · |

Ab7 · · · · | A7 · Ab7 · | Ema7 · · · · | D#mi7 · · · · | C#mi7 · · · · | C#mi7/B · · · · |

Bbmi7(b5) · · · · | Bbmi7/Ab · · · · | Eb7/G · · · · | Eb7 · · · · | Abmi7 · · · · | Abmi7/Gb · · · · |

D.C. AL CODA

Db7/F · · · · | Db7 · · · · | Ema7 · · · · | D#mi7 · · · · | C#mi7 · · · · | C9(#11) · · · · |

⊕ CODA

Bma7 · · · · | · · · · | C#mi7/B · · · · | · · · · | Bma7 · · · · | Cma7(#11) 𝆺 | Bma7 𝆺 |

PLAY 3 TIMES

Lyrics

THE FRIM FRAM SAUCE

I don't want french-fried potatoes, red ripe tomatoes.
I'm never satisfied.
I want the frim fram sauce with the oss and fay,
With shifafa on the side.

I don't want pork chops and bacon;
That won't awaken my appetite inside.
I want the frim fram sauce with the oss and fay,
With shifafa on the side.

Well, you know a girl, she really got to eat,
And a girl, she should eat right.
Five will get you ten;
I'm gonna feed myself right tonight.

I don't want fish cakes and rye bread;
You heard what I said.
Waiter, please, I want mine fried.
I want the frim fram sauce with the oss and fay,
With shifafa on the side.

SONG FOR MY FATHER

I wrote a song for my father
In hopes it would give him a thrill
After seeing Brazil.

My father's music came through me,
But never got to me until
I went down to Brazil.

In Rio all day long
I heard my father's song.
That bossa nova beat.
So sweet.

I heard the real bossa nova,
And never got over the thrill
When I went to Brazil.

No other people you meet
Play guitar with the beat and the skill
As they do in Brazil.

That Portuguese swing
Is such a subtle thing.
It makes you sway against your will.